When I get nervous, sometimes I fart. This has me really scared and very, VERY nervous about my first day of school.

Could I fart when I meet my teacher?

If I let one slip at a time that's not prudent
Will she think I am a terrible student?

On the playground
will I fart all around?

Could my back end blowout
be what everyone is talking about?

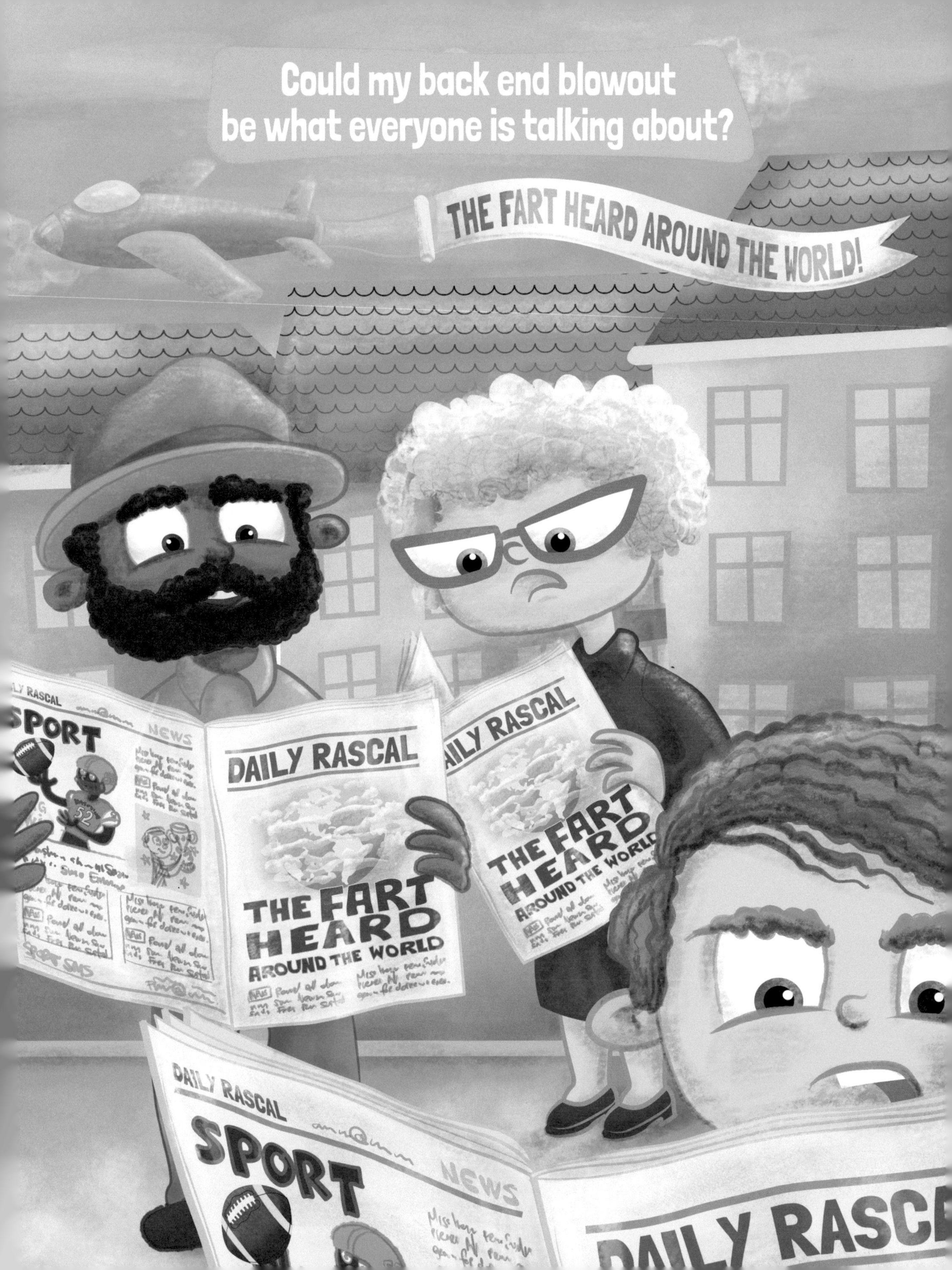

If I fart up at the chalkboard I would be floored!

When everyone is reading and being so quiet
Will my powerful poot start a laugh riot?

Maybe I could keep it in with a tight squeeze?
It's no use! I'll end up cutting the cheese.

Will I have so much thunder down under
that my first day is one big blunder?

What about gym class?

I just don't feel very brave
Because I don't think my booty will behave!

Could I fart in the car line or waiting for the bus?

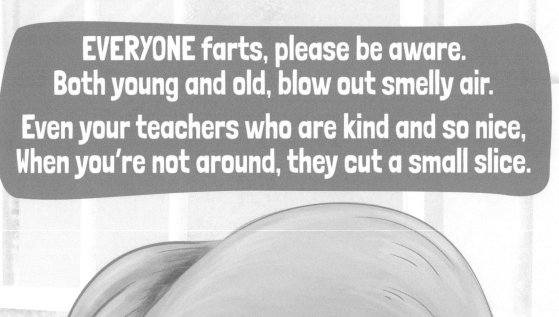

EVERYONE farts, please be aware.
Both young and old, blow out smelly air.

Even your teachers who are kind and so nice,
When you're not around, they cut a small slice.

We don't always know how things will go.
We might fear the worst, but you should know
that when you're not sure, and things seem scary,
All you can do is go through it. It's okay to be wary.

If the first day has you feeling nervous or shy,
The best thing to do is just give it a try

Your heart is brave and your brain is full of smarts
You won't be embarrassed by something silly...like **Farts!**

Made in United States
Troutdale, OR
08/09/2023